The children fed the hens.

They looked for eggs.

They put the eggs in a box.

Dad had an idea.

Kipper went on looking.

“Look at this egg,” said Kipper.

"This is too big."

Kipper looked at the hen.

“This is too big for you,” he said.

“Come and see this,” said Dad.

"This is too big for you," said Mum.

"This is too big for me," said Dad.